A.L.L.
to the Rescue

by Penelope Bradshaw
illustrated by Jackie Snider

HOUGHTON MIFFLIN HARCOURT
School Publishers

Printed in China

ISBN-10: 0-547-25313-3
ISBN-13: 978-0-547-25313-8

13 14 15 16 0940 19 18 17 16
4500569761

Act One

(A few pieces of litter are scattered throughout the stage. A bench sits near one end of the stage with a trash can in the opposite corner. A WORKER, wearing a hard hat, crosses the stage and plants a sign to one side.)

EASTLAKE PARK
UNDER CONSTRUCTION
CLOSED
UNTIL FURTHER NOTICE

(The WORKER *exits the stage as four kids appear on the opposite side:* LUCIA, MALIK, ABIGAIL, *and* WAYNE. *They walk toward the sign.* ABIGAIL *dribbles a ball. As they reach the sign,* LUCIA *holds up her arm to stop them, while pulling back on the leash of her dog. They stare at the sign without speaking for a moment and seem unable to move.)*

LUCIA: *(Somberly)* This is not good.

MALIK: This is not good at all.

WAYNE: *(Pointing at the locked gate)* The gate is locked. I guess that's to prevent burglaries of construction equipment.

ABIGAIL: Now where are we supposed to play ball?

MALIK: Where are we supposed to play, period?

LUCIA: Not here, I guess. *(Turns away from the sign)* Let's get out of here before we get depressed. *(They shuffle toward the bench and sit down, deflated. ABIGAIL takes a bag of carrots from her bag, has one, and passes it down the row. Each takes a carrot and chomps loudly.)*

LUCIA: We can't just sit by and let this happen. We've got to do something.

WAYNE: About what?

MALIK: The *park*. What else?

ABIGAIL: What can we do? The city has closed the park. Who knows when it will be open again?

EASTLAKE PARK
UNDER CONSTRUCTION
CLOSED
UNTIL FURTHER NOTICE

LUCIA: Isn't there anywhere else we can play? *(They pause to think.)*

WAYNE: In the street? *(The others turn to look at him.)*

MALIK: That's not a good option.

ABIGAIL: Unless you want to get flattened by a car. *(LUCIA looks up and scans the area. She squints her eyes and focuses on a spot in the near distance.)*

LUCIA: What about over there? *(They look up and follow her gaze.)*

WAYNE: The furniture store?

LUCIA: No, that grassy spot, right next to E.A.'s Ice Cream Treats.

ABIGAIL: The empty lot?

WAYNE: You mean—the dirty, empty lot?

MALIK: How would we play there? It's filled with litter.

LUCIA: I know, but if it weren't for the trash, it would be the perfect spot! *(They sit and think, downcast. WAYNE chomps loudly on a carrot.)*

MALIK: Hey, don't monopolize the carrots, Wayne!

WAYNE: Too late. *(At this, WAYNE looks around for a trash can to throw away the carrot bag, but there are none in sight.)*

WAYNE: No wonder there's litter. I suspect it's because there aren't any trash cans around.

LUCIA: Just put it in your pocket and throw it away later.

WAYNE: I will do that, but I am sure others would just throw the trash on the ground.

MALIK: Why do people litter?

WAYNE: I guess they must think everyone does it, so it's okay.

LUCIA: I've got an idea. I think we should organize a way to clean up the lot ourselves.

WAYNE: Pick up trash? Ew!

ABIGAIL: That's a great idea!

LUCIA: Who owns the lot?

MALIK: It's on the same property as the ice cream store, so I speculate it belongs to Mr. Jenkins. I wonder if he'll let us use it?

LUCIA: We'll just have to convince him. (ABIGAIL'S MOM *leans out the door of a house.*)

ABIGAIL'S MOM: Abigail! Have you finished your homework?

ABIGAIL: Uh, no—coming! *(Under her breath)* Do me a favor and call me later, and we can finish discussing this.

LUCIA: I'd better get home, too. (MALIK *nods as he and* LUCIA *quickly stand to go home.* WAYNE *hops up and runs after* LUCIA.)

WAYNE: Wait for me!

Act Two

(LUCIA, MALIK, ABIGAIL, *and* WAYNE *are at their own homes. Each has a phone.* MALIK *dials his as* LUCIA *and* ABIGAIL *already talk on the phone.* WAYNE *holds the handset to a video game, which he plays.*)

ABIGAIL: What if we told Mr. Jenkins that we were assisting in the war against litter?

LUCIA: How can you have a war against something that can't fight back? Litter is innocent. It's people who make litter.

ABIGAIL: Then we could call it a campaign—wait, Lucia, can you hold on a second? I'm getting another call. *(Clicks the phone over)* Hello?

MALIK: *(Into the phone)* Did you two think of anything good yet?

ABIGAIL: I was just suggesting we call it a campaign.

MALIK: Bo-ring!

ABIGAIL: Do you have a better idea, Einstein?

MALIK: Uh …

ABIGAIL: Now it's your turn to be enterprising. *(Clicks over while* MALIK *thinks)* That was Malik. He had a few criticisms to offer but no new ideas.

LUCIA: Have you talked to Wayne?

ABIGAIL: I'm sure he's busy saving the world—again— on that video game of his. *(*MALIK *begins to whistle impatiently.* WAYNE *plays his game more and more enthusiastically.)*

LUCIA: That's it! We'll make it into a game! Instead of a baseball or soccer league, it will be an Anti-Litter League—*A.L.L.!*

ABIGAIL: Excellent! I'll pass that on. *(Clicks over.* MALIK *makes a loud snoring noise.)* Hey, wake up, Malik— we've got it! We'll fill you in tomorrow before school. Tell Wayne to get there early. *(They hang up simultaneously.* MALIK *dials.* WAYNE *picks the phone up, still playing his game.)*

WAYNE: What's up?

Act Three, Scene One

(LUCIA, MALIK, ABIGAIL, *and* WAYNE *enter the ice cream parlor of* MR. JENKINS, *who sits in a chair, in front of a long panel of ice cream flavors. He looks downcast, as if he has a particularly cumbersome burden on his mind. No one else is in the store.*)

LUCIA: Mr. Jenkins?

MR. JENKINS: What? Oh, hello there. Did you kids come for some ice cream?

WAYNE: No, sir, actually—(ABIGAIL *shoots him a look.*)

ABIGAIL: *(Elbows him to stop talking)* Why, yes! We'd love some. (WAYNE *rubs his arm sorely.*)

MR. JENKINS: Oh, good, good. Some people say it's a little early for ice cream this time of year but not me! I say ice cream is good any time of the year! *(He stands up, cracking a tiny smile. He picks up a scoop.)*

MR. JENKINS: Now what would you like? *(The kids inspect the flavors.)*

WAYNE: I'd love a triple scoop of raspberry, strawberry, and mango sherbet, please. In a cone!

MR. JENKINS: You got it. (He puts three scoops of sherbet on a cone and hands it to him. The others look at him and shake their heads skeptically. He begins to eat ravenously.)

WAYNE: Mmm!

LUCIA: I'll have a scoop of chocolate yogurt in a cup, please.

MALIK and ABIGAIL: *(In unison)* I'll have vanilla with sprinkles! (MALIK *and* ABIGAIL *look at each other, slightly embarrassed.* MR. JENKINS *chuckles to himself.)*

MR. JENKINS I knew I hadn't misjudged you kids. Sounds like you both have good taste!

MR. JENKINS: *(Finishes scooping the kids' frozen yogurt and hands them out)* Is there anything else you'd like? *(They all eagerly eat their treats. LUCIA looks up nervously.)*

LUCIA: *(Stammers)* Well, uh, actually—we had an idea that we wanted to discuss with you.

MR. JENKINS: With me? What about?

MALIK: Well, you see, they shut down the park.

ABIGAIL: Also, you have this lot—

LUCIA: We were thinking that it would be a really good idea if …

WAYNE: We want to organize a competition to clean up your lot next door! It's called *A.L.L.*—the Anti-Litter League! Then we would have a place to play, and you would have tons of kids coming to buy ice cream. All we need prior to getting started is for you to give us permission.

MR. JENKINS: Whoa there! Slow down, friends. This scheme sounds interesting, very interesting, indeed.

ABIGAIL: We'll wear rubber gloves!

MALIK: Also, we'll sweep up the trash, and an adult will collect and dispose of it!

MR. JENKINS: You've thought of everything, have you? *(They nod, happily eating their ice cream.)*

MR. JENKINS: *A.L.L.* … hmm, I like the sound of that. This might just work.

Act Three, Scene Two

(Kids of all ages play in the newly cleaned up lot. A sign for E.A.'s Ice Cream Treats stands nearby. LUCIA, MALIK, ABIGAIL, and WAYNE stand together. WAYNE licks an ice cream cone.)

LUCIA: It's so nice to be outside!

MALIK: Yes, this is fun and all, but you know, in a way …

ABIGAIL: It's not quite as fun as *A.L.L.!*

LUCIA: *(Smiles)* I agree.

ABIGAIL: Now that we've taken care of this area, should we clean up another?

MALIK: *(Regretfully)* This is going to be one dirty business.

LUCIA: Yeah, but somebody's got to do it.

Responding

✔ **TARGET SKILL** **Theme** What do the thoughts and actions of the characters tell you about the theme of the play? What details support your conclusion? Copy and complete the chart below.

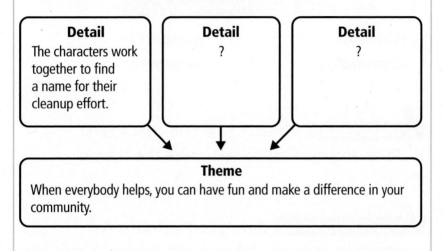

Detail
The characters work together to find a name for their cleanup effort.

Detail
?

Detail
?

Theme
When everybody helps, you can have fun and make a difference in your community.

Write About It

Text to World Write a letter to the editor of your local newspaper that describes a litter problem and your proposed solution.

TARGET VOCABULARY

assist	prior
burglaries	regretfully
favor	scheme
innocent	speculated
misjudged	suspect

EXPAND YOUR VOCABULARY

criticisms	property
monopolize	somberly

TARGET SKILL **Theme** Examine characters' qualities and motives to recognize the theme of the play.

TARGET STRATEGY **Analyze/Evaluate** Ask questions to analyze and evaluate the text's meaning.

GENRE A **play** tells a story through the words and actions of its characters.